# National Parks

## Parks

### Book of Days
#### by Adam Jones

Tide-mark Press
East Hartford, Connecticut

Published by Tide-mark Press Ltd., P.O. Box 280311, East Hartford, CT 06128-0311
Distributed in Canada by Monarch Books of Canada
Copyright 1996 by Adam Jones and Tide-mark Press Ltd.
Design and typography by Corry Kaeser Cote
Printed in Singapore by Craft Print
All Rights Reserved.
ISBN 1-55949-324-0
Cover photograph: Merced River flowing past
Upper Yosemite Falls, Yosemite National Park, California by Adam Jones

*The Watchman at first light. Zion National Park, Utah.*
*Photography by Adam Jones*

1

2

3

4

5

6

7

8

9

10

11

12

13

14

*Cypress trees and Giant Leather Ferns. Everglades National Park. Florida.*
*Photography by Adam Jones*

*Canyon walls. Grand Canyon National Park. Arizona.*
*Photography by Adam Jones*

15

16

17

18

19

20

21

22

23

24

25

26

27

28

*Snow-covered conifers. Great Smoky Mountains National Park. Tennessee.*
*Photography by Adam Jones*

*Sunset. Everglades National Park. Florida.*
*Photography by Adam Jones*

29

30

31

1

2

3

4

5

6

7

8

9

10

11

*Snake River at sunrise. Grand Teton National Park. Wyoming.*
*Photography by Adam Jones*

*Delicate Arch, Arches National Park, Utah.*
*Photography by Adam Jones*

12

13

14

15

16

17

18

19

20

21

22

23

24

25

*Hallett Peak rises over Bear Lake. Rocky Mountain National Park. Colorado.*
*Photography by Adam Jones*

*Mt. Shuksan mirrored in Picture Lake. North Cascades National Park. Washington.*
*Photography by Adam Jones*

*26*

*27*

*28*

*29*

*1*

*2*

*3*

*4*

*5*

*6*

*7*

*8*

*9*

*10*

*Violets and Spring Beauties. Daniel Boone National Forest. Kentucky.*
*Photography by Adam Jones*

*Merced River flowing past Upper Yosemite Falls. Yosemite National Park. California. Photography by Adam Jones*

11

12

13

14

15

16

17

18

19

20

21

22

23

24

*Dogwoods in bloom. Shenandoah National Park. Virginia.*
*Photography by Adam Jones*

*Redwood trees and ferns. Muir Woods National Monument. California.*
*Photography by Adam Jones*

25

26

27

28

29

30

31

1

2

3

4

5

6

7

"Hoodoos" formation viewed from Fairyland Point, Bryce Canyon National Park, Utah.
Photography by Adam Jones

*Bordered by asters, Reflection Lake twins Mt. Rainier.*
*Mt. Rainier National Park, Washington.*
*Photography by Adam Jones*

8

9

10

11

12

13

14

15

16

17

18

19

20

21

*Linn Cove Creek, Blue Ridge National Parkway, North Carolina.*
*Photography by Adam Jones*

*Along the south rim. Grand Canyon National Park. Arizona.*
*Photography by Adam Jones*

22

23

24

25

26

27

28

29

30

1

2

3

4

5

*The Bryce Amphitheater from Inspiration Point. Bryce Canyon National Park. Utah.*
*Photography by Adam Jones*

*Lower Yellowstone Falls. Yellowstone National Park. Wyoming.*
*Photography by Adam Jones*

6

7

8

9

10

11

12

13

14

15

16

17

18

19

Park Avenue formation, Arches National Park, Utah.
Photography by Adam Jones

*Cades Cove, Great Smokey Mountains National Park, Tennessee.*
*Photography by Adam Jones*

20

21

22

23

24

25

26

27

28

29

30

31

1

2

*Mt. Shuksan mirrored in Picture Lake. North Cascades National Park. Washington.*
*Photography by Adam Jones*

*Layered sandstone. Zion National Park. Utah.*
*Photography by Adam Jones*

3

4

5

6

7

8

9

*10*

*11*

*12*

*13*

*14*

*15*

*16*

*Morning Glory Pool. Yellowstone National Park. Wyoming.*
*Photography by Adam Jones*

*Schoodic Peninsula. Acadia National Park. Maine.*
*Photography by Adam Jones*

*17*

*18*

*19*

*20*

*21*

*22*

*23*

24

25

26

27

28

29

30

*Bear Lake, Rocky Mountain National Park, Colorado.*
*Photography by Adam Jones*

*Indian Paintbrush and Cow Parsnip in bloom on Hurricane
Ridge, Olympic National Park, Washington.
Photography by Adam Jones*

1

2

3

4

5

6

7

8

9

10

11

12

13

14

Sunrise silhouettes Old Faithful and a small herd
of bison. Yellowstone National Park. Wyoming.
Photography by Adam Jones

*Bridal Veil Falls and Cathedral Rocks, Yosemite National Park, California.*
*Photography by Adam Jones*

15

16

17

18

19

20

21

22

23

24

25

26

27

28

*Volcanic cinder cones, Haleakala Crater, Haleakala National Park, Hawaii.*
*Photography by Adam Jones*

*Delicate Arch and the distant La Sal Mountains, Arches National Park, Utah.*
*Photography by Adam Jones*

29

30

31

1

2

3

4

5

6

7

8

9

10

11

*Wonderland Trail. Mt. Rainier National Park. Washington.*
*Photography by Adam Jones*

*Zion National Park. Utah.*
*Photography by Adam Jones*

*12*

*13*

*14*

*15*

*16*

*17*

*18*

19

20

21

22

23

24

25

*Balsam Root flowering in Dunraven Pass, Yellowstone National Park, Wyoming.*
*Photography by Adam Jones*

*Beaver Pond at sunrise, Grand Teton National Park, Wyoming.*
*Photography by Adam Jones*

26

27

28

29

30

31

1

2

3

4

5

6

7

8

*Waves crashing on a beach of black volcanic sand.*
*Hawaii Volcanoes National Park. Hawaii.*
*Photography by Adam Jones*

*Autumn colors. Blue Ridge National Parkway. North Carolina.*
*Photography by Adam Jones*

*9*

*10*

*11*

*12*

*13*

*14*

*15*

16

17

18

19

20

21

22

*El Capitan. Yosemite National Park. California.*
*Photography by Adam Jones*

*Clouds fill the valley below Thomas Ridge.*
*Great Smoky Mountains National Park. Tennessee.*
*Photography by Adam Jones*

23

24

25

26

27

28

29

30

1

2

3

4

5

6

*Fall-tinted aspens. Grand Teton National Park. Wyoming.*
*Photography by Adam Jones*

*Colorado River, Glen Canyon National Recreation Area, Arizona.*
*Photography by Adam Jones*

7

8

9

10

11

12

13

14

15

16

17

18

19

20

*Looking toward Frenchman Bay From Cadillac Mountain.*
*Mt. Desert Island. Acadia National Park. Maine.*
*Photography by Adam Jones*

*Weathered pine tree, south rim of Grand Canyon National Park, Arizona.*
*Photography by Adam Jones*

21

22

23

24

25

26

27

28

29

30

31

1

2

3

*Rickrack fence. Hensley Settlement. Cumberland Gap National Historical Park. Kentucky.*
*Photography by Adam Jones*

*Nickel Creek, Mt. Rainier National Park, Washington.*
*Photography by Adam Jones*

4

5

6

7

8

9

10

11

12

13

14

15

16

17

*Sunrise. Cumberland Gap National Historical Park. Kentucky.*
*Photography by Adam Jones*

*Clouds above Mt. Hood. Mt. Hood National Forest. Oregon.*
*Photography by Adam Jones*

*18*

*19*

*20*

*21*

*22*

*23*

*24*

25

26

27

28

29

30

1

*Eco Pond. Everglades National Park. Florida.*
*Photography by Adam Jones*

*Luminous fall sky. Yellowstone National Park. Wyoming.*
*Photography by Adam Jones*

2

3

4

5

6

7

8

9

10

11

12

13

14

15

*Mt. Shuksan mirrored in Picture Lake. North Cascades National Park. Washington.*
*Photography by Adam Jones*

*Autumn leaves. Acadia National Park. Maine.*
*Photography by Adam Jones*

16

17

18

19

20

21

22

23

24

25

26

27

28

29

*Seastack silhouetted at sunset. Point of Arches. Olympic National Park. Washington.*
*Photography by Adam Jones*

*Cathedral Spires, Yosemite National Park, California.*
*Photography by Adam Jones*

*30*

*31*

*Save a picture or dry a flower here*

# Birthstones and Flowers

| Month | Stone | Flower |
|-------|-------|--------|
| January | Garnet | Carnation |
| February | Amethyst | Violet |
| March | Aquamarine | Jonquil |
| April | Diamond | Sweet Pea |
| May | Emerald | Daisy |
| June | Pearl | Rose |
| July | Ruby | Larkspur |
| August | Sardonyx | Gladiolus |
| September | Sapphire | Lavender |
| October | Opal | Aster |
| November | Topaz | Chrysanthemum |
| December | Turquoise | Holly |

# Wedding Anniversaries

| | | | |
|---|---|---|---|
| First | Paper | Thirteenth | Lace |
| Second | Cotton | Fourteenth | Ivory |
| Third | Leather | Fifteenth | Crystal |
| Fourth | Books | Twentieth | China |
| Fifth | Wood or Clocks | Twenty-fifth | Silver |
| Sixth | Iron | Thirtieth | Pearl |
| Seventh | Copper. Bronze or Brass | Thirty-fifth | Coral or Jade |
| Eighth | Electrical Appliances | Fortieth | Ruby |
| Ninth | Pottery | Forty-fifth | Sapphire |
| Tenth | Tin or Aluminum | Fiftieth | Gold |
| Eleventh | Steel | Fifty-fifth | Emerald |
| Twelfth | Silk or Linen | Sixtieth | Diamond |

# About the Author

For the past 15 years Adam Jones has worked continually to perfect his craft. Today his nature photographs are seen regularly in prestigious national and international publications. Ranging in scope from wildlife to sweeping landscapes, Adam's photographs are found in a wide variety of consumer and commercial publications, including posters, greeting cards, magazines, billboards, text books, calendars, advertising, and annual reports for major corporations.

As a writer and nature photojournalist, Adam's articles on travel destinations and natural history subjects are found in national magazines such as Outdoor Photographer, Birder's World, Michigan Living, and Petersen's Photographic.

Other publication credits include: National Wildlife Federation, Natural History, National Geographic, Backpacker, Hallmark Cards, Gibson Greetings, Readers Digest Books, Greenpeace, Country, Outdoor Photographer, Falcon Press, Ideals, Chicadee, and hundreds of text books.

Adam's photographic expertise and genuine desire to help others have earned him a reputation as a top-notch photographic workshop and tour leader. For more information about workshops and tours featuring Adam Jones, please contact Nature's Light at: (513) 793-2346.

For information on these and other stock images by Adam Jones, contact: Adam Jones, 3415 Rems Road, Louisville, KY 40241, or fax him at: (502) 327-8032.

# National Parks

Acadia National Park
P.O. Box 177
Bar Harbor. ME 04609

Arches National Park
P.O. Box 907
Moab. Utah 84532

Blue Ridge National Parkway
200 BB&T Building
One Pack Square
Asheville. NC 28801

Bryce Canyon National Park
Bryce Canyon. UT 84717

Cumberland Gap National Historical Park
P.O. Box 1848
Middlesboro. KY 40965

Everglades National Park
40001 State Rd. 9336
Homestead. FL 33034

Glen Canyon National Recreation Area
P.O. Box 1507
Page. AZ 86040

Grand Canyon National Park
P.O. Box 129
Grand Canyon. AZ 86023

Grand Teton National Park
P.O. Drawer 170
Moose. WY 83012

Great Smoky Mountains National Park
Gatlinburg. TN 37738

Haleakala National Park
P.O. Box 369
Makawao. HI 96768

Hawaii Volcanoes National Park
P.O. Box 52
Hawaii National Park. HI 96718

Mount Rainier National Park
Tahoma Woods. Star Route
Ashford. WA 98304

Muir Woods National Monument
Mill Valley. CA 94941

North Cascades Nationall Park
2105 Highway 20
Sedro Woolley. WA 98284

Olympic National Park
600 East Park Ave.
Port Angeles. WA 98362

Rocky Mountain National Park
Estes Park. CO 80517

Shenandoah Nationall Park
Route 4. Box 348
Luray. VA 22835

Yellowstone National Park
P.O. Box 168
Yellowstone National Park. WY 82190

Yosemite National Park
P.O. Box 577
Yosemite National Park. CA 95389

Zion National Park
Springdale. UT 86767-1099